Enid Blyton's

NODDY

Plays Hide-and-Seek

A Lift-the-Flap Book

BBC CHILDREN'S BOOKS

Noddy and his friends are having a game of hide-and-seek.
They're all running off to hide.

Ah ha! Noddy can see the end
of Bumpy Dog's tail.

The Skittles have found a very good hiding-place in the market, but Noddy thinks he can find them.

Noddy can see two hats.

Noddy thinks he knows where Big-Ears
and Dinah are hiding.

Noddy is sure there's someone hiding in the Noah's Ark.

He can hear someone giggling from behind the hedge.

Noddy thinks he might find someone in the farmyard.

Mr Tubby Bear is too big to hide properly.

Noddy can't find Sammy Sailor, but he's sure that he's here somewhere.